Phillipkennedy.
Phillip

The publishers wish to acknowledge the kind assistance of
Mr Michael Chinery in the preparation of this book.

Copyright © 1979, 1984 by Grisewood & Dempsey Ltd.

Published in this edition by Galley Press,
an imprint of W.H. Smith and Son Limited,
Registered No. 237811 England.
Trading as WHS Distributors, St John's House,
East Street, Leicester, LE1 6NE.

ISBN 0 86136 845 2

Printed and bound in Portugal by Printer Portuguesa, Sintra.

The Otter

By Angela Sheehan
Illustrated by Bernard Robinson

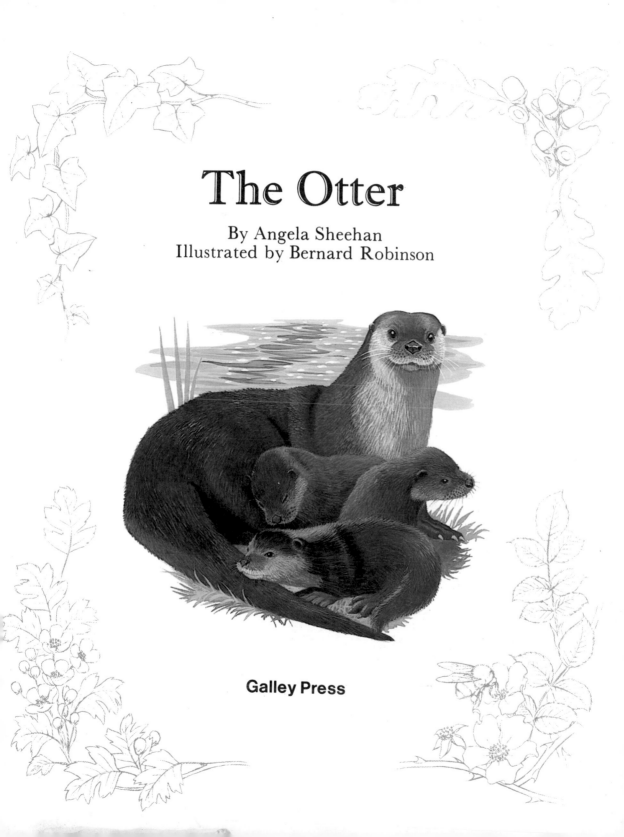

Galley Press

With one slight, swift movement, the otter slipped into the water. She made no noise and her sleek body hardly disturbed the still surface of the pool. Only a few ripples lapped their way to the muddy bank. Then all was calm, until the same thin ripples spread out again a short distance away, and the otter surfaced. As the animal swam to the bank, the moonlight caught the silvery scales of the fish she gripped in her mouth. But the otter did not linger in the light. She slid into the shelter of the reeds and ate her tasty roach.

When she had finished the fish, the otter set off along the river bank. By morning light, she was far from the hole where she had spent the day before. But she had no need to return to that hole. There were plenty more places along the river where she could rest.

As soon as she found a hole, the otter pushed her way in. The moss-lined tunnel was dark and narrow, and the entrance was so small that it squeezed the water out of her furry coat.

All day she slept in the hole. No light reached her, but she had plenty of air. The otter that had dug the hole in the first place had made a shaft to the surface to let in air.

All through the autumn, she spent the daytime curled up in a hole. And at night she wandered along the river, finding fishes, frogs, shellfish and insects to eat.

Soon the reeds by the water's edge turned brown. The leaves fell from the alders and poplars that grew along the bank. The frogs dug themselves into the soft mud. Winter had come.

When the river froze over the otter had to swim under the ice to catch her food. It was hard work for her. She could only swim a little way before running out of air. Then she had to hurry back to the breathing hole she had made in the ice. Night after night, the ceiling of ice on the river grew thicker. It was time for her to find a better stretch of water.

The otter set off early in the evening.
Keeping close to the hedges, she crossed one snowy
field after another. By dawn, she had reached the
top of a high hill, and she could see a broad river
below her. It was still flowing. The otter ran as fast
as she could down through the meadows.

At the top of the bank, she stopped, sank to her stomach, and launched herself over the edge. Down she went, down the steep, slippery slope, faster and faster. At the bottom she came to a halt, panting. She rested for a moment, then stretched herself ready to plunge into the river. But she did not plunge. Instead, she turned, raced back up the slope and slid all the way down again. This made the slope even more slippery, and even better for tobogganing. Time and again the otter launched herself down the slide.

By the time she stopped her games, the otter was too tired to swim or catch fish. She wanted only to sleep. So she found a hollow in some bushes on the bank and soon fell fast asleep.

That evening she woke, hungry and stiff. Again she slid down the slope, but this time she did not run back again. She plunged straight into the river. She caught two sticklebacks, and swallowed them as she swam. Farther downstream she came upon some eels, her favourite food. She caught the wriggling creatures, one after another, dragging them from the water with her sharp teeth.

Night after night, she travelled farther downstream. The river grew wider and wider, and the water tasted more and more salty. The banks of the river grew flatter and soon disappeared altogether. The otter had reached the sea. It was almost morning and time to find a hiding place. But there were no otter holes on the shore. So she braved the daylight in the water. She swam in the shallows, twisting and turning and rolling about in the waves.

Later in the day, she rested among the tangled seaweeds on the rocks. Then, watched by a crowd of gulls and oyster catchers, she caught some food: shrimps and mussels and lots of little fishes. Everything was new.

After a few days, the otter had still not found a really comfortable place in which to sleep. The sea made her feel tired, and she longed to drink fresh river water again and rest in a warm burrow. So she left the sea and made her way upstream.

Before long the mud flats by the river gave way to tree-lined banks. And the otter was able to spend her third day upstream snug among the roots of a willow tree. She did not know that a male otter was sleeping only a short way away. In the evening the two left their hiding places at the same time. They chased the same fish and watched each other as they swam. They raced each other to catch a duck. They scampered across the marshy banks and dived back into the water. The female chased the male, and he chased her. They were so busy with their games that they hardly ate at all.

By daybreak, they had moved even farther
upstream. There the two stayed. At night, they
caught birds, frogs and fish. They often played
together in the water or on the bank. During the
day, they each found a hole to sleep in; and if they
could not find one, they dug one.

One night, the two otters noticed some fine big salmon swimming rapidly upstream. They each raced after one of them. The male snatched at his first, but he only managed to grip a fin in his mouth. The fish wrenched its body away and swam for its life. The female sank her sharp teeth into the body of her salmon and managed to hold on to it, while it fought to get away. Slowly the fish stopped wrestling and died. The otter dragged her prize from the water and settled down to eat it.

While the otter ate the salmon, her male playmate watched from the other side of the river. Then he swam across the water and slowly crept towards her. She was too busy to see him or hear his light tread. He waited quivering nearby, making a soft squeaking noise. The female heard the noise and greeted the male by squeaking back to him. He edged forward and bit into the salmon.

By now, she had eaten quite enough so she went for a swim while the male ate. Even he could not finish so large a fish. Its half-eaten body lay on the bank, a mess of bones, scales and blood, when he took to the water. His playmate greeted him and they swam lazily together as the early morning sun rose above the dark, bare branches. They did not go straight to their burrows that morning. Instead they played for a while and then mated.

Six weeks later, the female left the river.
She climbed the bank and searched the dense
undergrowth for a place to dig her holt. Her mate
stayed by the river, but still saw her as she came
and went to her new home. One night, she did not
come to the river to eat. She stayed in the holt. The
time had come to give birth to her cubs.

Deep in the warm burrow, the tiny blind cubs snuggled up to their mother's fur. They sucked milk from her body and slept all day and all night. Their father never saw them. But sometimes he brought a frog or a fish to the mouth of the holt for his mate to eat. It was hungry work for her, feeding the cubs and having little to eat herself.

It was two whole months before the tiny cubs made their way to the holt's entrance. Their mother urged them on but they were too scared to go far. They were also too scared to be left behind when she went off to fish. So in the end they had to follow her. They had never seen the light. Every sight, sound and smell was strange. But they enjoyed running along behind their mother. And when they came to the edge of the bank, they slid down behind her.

But as soon as they came to the water's edge they stopped. The waves lapped over their feet and made them cold and wet. The wind whistled across the surface and ruffled their coats. Their mother dived in but the three youngsters stayed on the bank, huddled together. So she climbed out of the water, nudged them apart and gently pushed them down to the brink. Suddenly one of the cubs lost his footing on the bank and tumbled into the water.

He clutched wildly at a water plant and squeaked with fear but nothing could save him now. He was in the water. But it was not so frightening after all; in fact, it felt warm and smooth, and he could swim. Slowly, the other two cubs were coaxed to follow him by their mother.

Once all three were in the water, they had a
fine time, diving, splashing, leaping and plunging.
They swam along behind their mother like
ducklings and jumped on her back for a ride.

The otter cubs loved the water, but they
could not stay there all the time. They explored the
fields by the holt, finding new things to eat every
night. They ate insects and slugs and worms and
frogs. One of the females even became quite skilled
at catching voles.

The cubs never saw their father. Their
mother no longer needed him, so he made his way
downstream. Next year he would find a new mate,
and so would she.

During the winter, the rest of the family snuggled up in a new burrow nearer the river. They went out each night but still kept close together. One windy evening, just as they were about to leave the burrow, they heard a loud groaning noise and the ground seemed to shudder. Suddenly a great tree root ripped through the wall of the burrow and the otter's home caved in. An old willow tree had been uprooted by the gale. The animals struggled through the falling earth to get clear of the root. They tumbled out of their home, bruised and shaken.

The two female cubs whimpered at their mother's side. The young male cub was nowhere to be seen. He had been at the very end of the tunnel and was now cut off, buried beneath the crushing weight of the tree. Outside, the earth was still shifting and soil and stones were hailing down the slope. The three otters headed for the water and swam as fast and as far as they could.

It seemed a long time before the fallen tree came to rest. The young otter, buried alive far below the surface, waited in terror. Soon there was silence and stillness. The little otter scratched above his head and saw a tiny beam of light. The shaft his mother had made to let in air had held firm despite the upheaval. The otter tried to widen the narrow tube. He worked slowly, scraping the soil with his paws.

After several hours, his body felt stiff and
his paws were sore. But he was free and alive. The
others were far away. He would never see them
again. He swam to the far bank of the river, and
slept curled up under an alder. The next night he
must set off on his own to see the world.

That same night, the otter and the two
female cubs left the river and made their way
overland to a small pool. Throughout the winter
they stayed together helping each other to find food
and shelter.

In spring the warm weather came. The otter wandered far from the pool. She often went to the big river where the eels were again making their way upstream. The young females liked to find holes for themselves now. They, too, wandered far. One found her way to the big river, the other to a stream even farther away.

The otter's family had gone for good now. Soon it would be time for her to find another mate and rear another family. The young females, too, would be ready to mate, and so would their brother, far, far away.

More About Otters

Eyes on top of head so the otter can see above the water

Nose high up so the otter can breathe while swimming

Whiskers long and sensitive to vibrations in the water.

Teeth strong and sharp for holding and biting flesh and cracking shellfish

Ears which can be sealed underwater

Tail long and flexible for use as a rudder

Back feet webbed for paddling

Front feet with claws for digging

The body of the common otter.

The otter in the story is the common otter. It lives in Europe, parts of Asia and the northern tip of Africa. Another well known species is the Canadian otter which lives in North America. The two species look alike and live in a similar way.

Acrobats in the Water
The otter is perfectly suited for its life in the water. Its eyes have special lenses so that it can see clearly underwater. When the water is too murky, the otter can feel its way with its long sensitive whiskers. Its eyes and nostrils are on the top of its head so it can see above the surface of the water and breathe without lifting its head above the surface.

The otter has two types of fur; long 'guard hairs' which are kept oily by special glands in the skin and, underneath, a fluffy coat which stays warm and dry in the water because of the protective outer hairs.

The otter's slim body and flat head allow it to slip easily through the water. When it swims on the surface of the water it paddles with its powerful webbed back feet. Swimming underwater it draws its legs into its body and moves by wriggling its tail and body like an eel. It can change direction quickly, roll over and turn very small circles using its tail as a rudder.

Night Prowlers
Fish and other small water animals are the otter's main food. It usually feeds at night and is a swift, cunning hunter. One of its tricks is to swim up behind a fish so that the fish cannot see it. It also swims round in circles at the bottom of the river to stir the little fishes out of the mud. Otters have been known to swim underneath ducks and pull them underwater. Even out of the water they are skilful hunters, catching and eating small rodents.

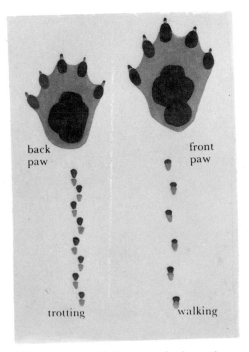

back paw

front paw

trotting

walking

If you see any of these tracks by a river, watch carefully and quietly and you may be lucky enough to see an otter.

Otters in Danger

Otters are hunted for their fur, especially in cold northern regions where the fur grows thicker. Because of this, even the well known types of otter are hard to find now. Other types, such as the small clawed otter of India and Asia, the clawless otter of Africa and the giant Brazilian otter are very rare indeed.

The sea otter in the picture is shorter and fatter than river otters. It lives, breeds and eats in the sea. It even sleeps in the sea, wrapping seaweed around its body to stop it from floating away. When it eats, it floats on its back and uses its belly as a table. It breaks open the shellfish it likes by smashing them with a stone.

Tracks and Signs

Otters are shy animals so they are difficult to spot. But you can tell where they have been because they leave tracks and signs behind them. When the ground is soft you can see the paw prints they have made.

If you see a half eaten fish or some shells on a rock sticking up out of the water, it may be what is left of an otter's dinner. Otters also leave their droppings, or spraints, in special places to mark out their territories.

If you are lucky, you may find an otter 'slide' like the one in the story. You may even find an otter's holt. Holts are burrows in the river bank, often with an underwater entrance and a shaft to the surface to let in air.

The sea otter with its 'table' set for lunch.